Microsoft® Access® 2016

Workbook

Nita Rutkosky
Pierce College at Puyallup
Puyallup, Washington

Audrey Roggenkamp
Pierce College at Puyallup
Puyallup, Washington

Ian Rutkosky
Pierce College at Puyallup
Puyallup, Washington

PARADIGM
EDUCATION SOLUTIONS

St. Paul

Senior Vice President	Linda Hein
Editor in Chief	Christine Hurney
Director of Production	Timothy W. Larson
Production Editors	Rachel Kats, Jen Weaverling
Cover and Text Designer	Valerie King
Copy Editor	Sarah Kearin
Senior Design and Production Specialist	Jaana Bykonich
Assistant Developmental Editors	Mamie Clark, Katie Werdick
Testers	Desiree Carvel; Ann E. Mills, Ivy Tech Community College of Indiana, Indianapolis, IN
Instructional Support Writer	Brienna McWade
Indexer	Terry Casey
Vice President Information Technology	Chuck Bratton
Digital Projects Manager	Tom Modl
Vice President Sales and Marketing	Scott Burns
Director of Marketing	Lara Weber McLellan

Care has been taken to verify the accuracy of information presented in this book. However, the authors, editors, and publisher cannot accept responsibility for Web, email, newsgroup, or chat room subject matter or content, or for consequences from application of the information in this book, and make no warranty, expressed or implied, with respect to its content.

Trademarks: Some of the product names and company names included in this book have been used for identification purposes only and may be trademarks or registered trade names of their respective manufacturers and sellers. Access, Excel, Internet Explorer, Microsoft, PowerPoint, and Windows are trademarks of Microsoft Corporation in the United States and/or other countries. The authors, editors, and publisher disclaim any affiliation, association, or connection with, or sponsorship or endorsement by, such owners.

Cover Photo Credits: © whitehoune/Shutterstock.com; © Fuatkose/iStock.com

We have made every effort to trace the ownership of all copyrighted material and to secure permission from copyright holders. In the event of any question arising as to the use of any material, we will be pleased to make the necessary corrections in future printings. Thanks are due to the aforementioned authors, publishers, and agents for permission to use the materials indicated.

ISBN: 978-0-76387-143-7 (print)
ISBN: 978-0-76386-716-4 (digital)

© 2017 by Paradigm Publishing, Inc.
875 Montreal Way
St. Paul, MN 55102
Email: educate@emcp.com
Website: ParadigmCollege.com

Printed in the United States of America

24 23 22 21 20 19 18 17   5 6 7 8 9 10 11 12

Microsoft® Access®

Study Tools

Study tools include a presentation and In Brief step lists. Use these resources to help you further develop and review skills learned in this section.

Knowledge Check

 SNAP Check your understanding by identifying application tools used in this section. If you are a SNAP user, launch the Knowledge Check from your Assignments page.

Recheck

 SNAP Check your understanding by taking this quiz. If you are a SNAP user, launch the Recheck from your Assignments page.

Skills Exercise

 SNAP Additional activities are available to SNAP users. If you are a SNAP user, access these activities from your Assignments page.

Skills Review

Review 1 Adjusting Column Widths; Finding and Editing Records; Adding and Deleting Records

Data File

1. Open **1-WEEmployees.accdb** and enable the contents, if necessary.
2. Open the Employees table.
3. Adjust all column widths to accommodate the longest entries.
4. Find the record for Carl Zakowski and then change the birth date from *5/9/1967* to *12/22/1987*.
5. Find the record for Roman Deptulski and then change the salary from *$69,725.00* to *$72,750.00*. ***Note: You do not need to type the dollar symbol, comma, decimal, or digits after the decimal point***.
6. Find the record for Terry Yiu and then change the hire date from *4/12/2012* to *1/31/2018*.
7. Delete the record for Valerie Fitsouris.
8. Delete the record for Edward Thurston.

9. Add the following records to the table in the appropriate fields.
   Note: In this table, **EmployeeID** *is not an AutoNumber data type field; therefore, you will need to type the numbers in the first field.*

1085	1090	1095
Yousef J Armine	Maria D Quinte	Patrick J Kilarney
11/19/1992	4/16/1993	2/27/1987
3/14/2018	11/29/2018	12/12/2018
European Distribution	Overseas Distribution	North American Distribution
$42,177	$42,177	$42,177

10. Close the Employees table. Click Yes when prompted to save changes.

 **Worldwide Enterprises**

Review 2 Sorting; Previewing; Changing Margins and Page Orientation; Filtering; Hiding Columns; Printing

1. With **1-WEEmployees.accdb** open, open the Employees table.
2. Sort the table in ascending order by *LastName*.
3. Preview the table in the Print Preview window.
4. Change to landscape orientation.
5. Change the top margin to 1.5 inches and the left margin to 1.25 inches using options at the Page Setup dialog box with the Print Options tab selected.
6. Print the table.
7. Filter the table to display only those employees who work in the European Distribution Department.
8. Hide the *EmployeeID* field column.
9. Print the table and then close the Employees table. Click Yes when prompted to save changes.
10. Close **1-WEEmployees.accdb**.

Skills Assessment

 **NIAGARA PENINSULA COLLEGE**

Data File

Assessment 1 Adjusting Column Width; Finding and Editing Records; Previewing and Printing

1. Open **1-NPCGrades.accdb** and enable the contents, if necessary.
2. Open the SM100-01Grades table.
3. Adjust all column widths to accommodate the longest entries.
4. Enter the following grades in the appropriate records:

Terry Yiu	A+	Kevin Gibson	C
Maren Bastow	C	Ash Bhullar	A
Martine Gagne	B	Bruce Morgan	B
Armado Ennis	D	Russell Clements	A
Bentley Woollatt	B	Richard Loewen	F
Susan Retieffe	C		

5. Preview and then print the table.
6. Close the SM100-01Grades table. Click Yes when prompted to save changes.
7. Close **1-NPCGrades.accdb**.

Assessment 2   Finding, Adding, and Deleting Records; Formatting Datasheet

1. Open **1-WBInventory.accdb** and enable the contents, if necessary.
2. Open the InventoryList table.
3. Adjust all column widths to accommodate the longest entry.
4. Locate and then delete the records for the inventory items *Pita Wraps*, *Tuna*, and *Lake Erie Perch*.
5. Add the following new records to the InventoryList table.

ItemNo	ItemDescription	Unit	SupplierCode
051	Atlantic Scallops	case	9
052	Lake Trout	case	9
053	Panini Rolls	flat	1

6. Change the font size for all data in the table to 10 points.
7. Preview the table in Print Preview and, if necessary, adjust the top and/or bottom margin settings until all of the records will print on one page and then print the table.
8. Close the InventoryList table. Click Yes when prompted to save changes.
9. Close **1-WBInventory.accdb**.

Assessment 3   Finding, Sorting, Filtering, and Deleting Records

1. Open **1-PTCostumeInv.accdb** and enable the contents, if necessary.
2. Open the CostumeInventory table.
3. Adjust all column widths to accommodate the longest entry.
4. Locate and then delete the records for the following costumes that were destroyed in a fire at a Shakespearean festival:

Macbeth	Othello
Lady Macbeth	King Lear
Hamlet	Richard III

5. Sort the table in ascending order by the *CostumeTitle* field.
6. Preview the table, adjust the margins so that all data fits on one page, and then print the table.
7. Filter the table so that only those records that were rented out on 10/1/2018 are displayed.
8. Print the filtered list.
9. Redisplay all records.
10. Clear the filter from the table.
11. Close the CostumeInventory table. Click Yes when prompted to save changes.
12. Close **1-PTCostumeInv.accdb**.

Assessment 4   Using the Filter by Form Feature

1. Using the Access Help window, locate and then open the article *Filter data in a desktop database*. Scroll down the article and locate the information on different ways to filter. Learn specifically how to use the Filter by Form feature.
2. Open **1-NPCGrades.accdb** and enable the contents, if necessary.
3. Open the AC215-03Grades table.

4. Using the Filter by Form feature, filter those records with a grade of *A+* or *F*.
5. Print the filtered table.
6. Clear the filter from the table.
7. Close the table without saving changes and then close the database.
8. Open Microsoft Word and then use one of the memo templates to create a memo addressed to your instructor that lists the steps you completed to filter the grades using the Filter by Form feature.
9. Save the memo and name it **1-FilterMemo**.
10. Print and then close **1-FilterMemo.docx**.
11. Close Word.

Assessment 5   Creating a Job Search Company Database

1. You are starting to plan ahead for your job search after graduation. You decide to maintain a database of company information in Access. To begin, search the Internet for at least eight companies in your field of study (four out of state or out of province). Include company name, address, and telephone number, and a contact person in the Human Resources Department, if possible.
2. Open **1-JobSearchInfo.accdb** and enable the contents, if necessary.
3. Open the CompanyInfo table. (The table contains eight records; you will be adding at least eight additional records.)
4. Enter at least eight additional records for the companies you researched on the Internet.
5. Adjust column widths as necessary.
6. Sort the records in ascending order by the *CompanyName* field.
7. Preview the table and make any changes required to ensure that the table prints on one page.
8. Print and then close the CompanyInfo table.
9. Close **1-JobSearchInfo.accdb**.

Marquee Challenge

Challenge 1   Updating and Printing a Catering Events Table

1. Open **1-WBSpecialEvents.accdb** and enable the contents, if necessary.
2. Open the CateringContracts table.
3. Dana Hirsch, manager, has given you information related to five new catering events that were recently booked at the bistro. Dana would like you to add to the table the information shown in Figure WB-1.1. Dana advises that deposits have been received for all of these events. The columns in the table that have check boxes displayed are defined as Yes/No fields. In these columns, click to insert a check mark in the box indicating "Yes"; otherwise leave the check box empty to indicate "No."
4. Jack Torrance has called and canceled his business meeting on May 15. Delete the record.

5. Dana would like the charge for the Pavelich wedding updated to $33.50 per person.
6. Dana would like a printout of the table with the records sorted by customers' last names and the *ID* and *ContactPhone* fields hidden.
7. Make sure the data is entirely visible in all columns and that the printout is only one page, and then print the table.
8. Close the CateringContracts table, saving design changes.
9. Close **1-WBSpecialEvents.accdb**.

Figure WB-1.1 Challenge 1

Name	Phone	Event	Date	Room	Guests	Charge	Special Menu
Cora Spriet	905 555 1623	Wedding	8/4/2018	Westview	150	26.95	Yes
Sean Vezina	716 555 3846	Business Meeting	8/13/2018	Starlake	24	23.75	No
William Graham	716 555 8694	25th Wedding Anniversary	8/18/2018	Sunset	80	24.95	No
Helen Kosjovic	716 555 3441	Engagement Brunch	8/19/2018	Sunset	56	22.95	No
Pieter Borman	716 555 6994	Business Meeting	8/22/2018	Starlake	41	24.95	Yes

 **Challenge 2**   Determining Fields and Table Names for a New Database

1. Bobbie Sinclair, business manager, is considering having you create a new database to store the custom costume business at Performance Threads. Bobbie has jotted down rough notes regarding the information to be stored in the new database in Figure WB-1.2. Using Microsoft Word, create a document that provides the proposed field names and table names for each table. Incorporate the information in the additional notes as you develop the tables. As you create this document, consider the following two database design practices:
   • The use of spaces in field names or table names is discouraged.
   • Within each table, one field must contain unique identifying information.
2. At this stage of the design process, you are only considering the breakdown of fields to accommodate the information in Figure WB-1.2. Do not be concerned with other elements of the table and database design, such as data type, properties, and relationships.
3. Save the Word document and name it **1-PTCostumes**.
4. Print and then close the document.

Figure WB-1.2 Challenge 2

Customer Information	Order Information
Customer's name, address, contact telephone numbers	Description of costume Customer for whom costume is being made Contract price Date due Seamstress Estimated hours for each of the main cost centers: Research, Design, Production Deposit amount received in advance
Contract Seamstresses Name, address, and contact telephone numbers for seamstresses on contract with Performance Threads	**Ship To Information** Customer Costume Address for delivery of costume Shipping company Shipping charge

Additional notes:
- Costumes are quoted a contract price, which the customer accepts in advance by signing a contract document. The signed document must be on file before work begins.
- The hours for the three cost centers are estimated at the time of the quote. Bobbie wants to use the database to also enter actual hours after the costume is complete to generate hours-variance reports.

Study Tools

Study tools include a presentation and In Brief step lists. Use these resources to help you further develop and review skills learned in this section.

Knowledge Check

SNAP Check your understanding by identifying application tools used in this section. If you are a SNAP user, launch the Knowledge Check from your Assignments page.

Recheck

SNAP Check your understanding by taking this quiz. If you are a SNAP user, launch the Recheck from your Assignments page.

Skills Exercise

SNAP Additional activities are available to SNAP users. If you are a SNAP user, access these activities from your Assignments page.

Skills Review

Review 1   Creating and Modifying a Table in Design View

Data File

1. Open **2-WEEmployeeData.accdb** and enable the contents, if necessary.
2. Create a table in Design view using the following field names and data types. You decide whether to add an appropriate description. Do *not* set any field properties since these will be changed later in this activity.

Field Name	Data Type
EmployeeID	Short Text
SupervisorLName	Short Text
SupervisorFName	Short Text
AnnualRevDate	Date/Time
SalaryIncDate	Date/Time
ProfDevDays	Number

3. Set the *EmployeeID* field as the primary key field.
4. Save the table and name it *Review*.

5. Switch to Datasheet view and then enter the following two records:

EmployeeID	1013	*EmployeeID*	1030
SupervisorLName	Vestering	*SupervisorLName*	Deptulski
SupervisorFName	Sam	*SupervisorFName*	Roman
AnnualRevDate	2/10/18	*AnnualRevDate*	1/22/19
SalaryIncDate	9/01/18	*SalaryIncDate*	7/22/19
ProfDevDays	5	*ProfDevDays*	10

6. Adjust all columns to best fit the longest entries.
7. Save the changes to the table layout.
8. Switch to Design view and then make the following changes to the field properties:
   a. Change the field size for the *EmployeeID* field to 4 characters.
   b. Create a validation rule for the *ProfDevDays* field to ensure that no number greater than 10 is entered into the field. Enter an appropriate validation text error message.
   c. Save the table and click Yes at the message that indicates some data may be lost and to test the data with the new validation rule.
   d. Create an input mask for both date fields to set the pattern for entering dates to the Medium Date format. Use the default entry for the placeholder character. Click Yes if prompted to save the table before displaying the Input Mask Wizard.
   e. Change the setting in the *Format* property box so both date fields display the date in the Medium Date format.
9. Save the table.
10. Switch to Datasheet view and add the following two records:

EmployeeID	1040	*EmployeeID*	1043
SupervisorLName	Ruiz	*SupervisorLName*	Deptulski
SupervisorFName	Celesta	*SupervisorFName*	Roman
AnnualRevDate	10-Mar-19	*AnnualRevDate*	15-Aug-18
SalaryIncDate	01-Sep-19	*SalaryIncDate*	01-Feb-19
ProfDevDays	8	*ProfDevDays*	6

11. Display the table in Print Preview.
12. Change to landscape orientation and then print the table.
13. Close Print Preview and then close the Review table.

Review 2   Modifying, Moving, and Deleting Fields; Creating Relationships

1. With **2-WEEmployeeData.accdb** open, open the Review table in Design view.
2. Move the *ProfDevDays* field between *SupervisorFName* and *AnnualRevDate*.
3. Move *SupervisorFName* before *SupervisorLName*.
4. Add caption properties so the fields display the following headings in Datasheet view:

   Supervisor First Name   *Annual Review Date*
   Supervisor Last Name   *Salary Increase Date*
   Professional Development Days

5. Save the table, switch to Datasheet view, adjust all column widths as necessary, and then print the datasheet in landscape orientation and with the left and right margins set to 0.5 inch.

6. Close the Review table, saving changes to the layout.
7. Open the Employees table in Design view.
8. Delete the *Supervisor* field.
9. Save and then close the Employees table.
10. Open the Relationships window.
11. Click the Show Table button in the Relationships group on the Relationship Tools Design tab, add the Review table to the window, and then close the Show Table dialog box.
12. Create a one-to-one relationship between the Employees table (primary table) and the Review table (related table) using the *EmployeeID* field. Turn on referential integrity.
13. Save the changes to the relationships.
14. Generate a new relationship report and then print the report in landscape orientation.
15. Save the new report, naming it *Relationships*, and then close the report.
16. Close the Relationships window and then close **2-WEEmployeeData.accdb**.

Skills Assessment

NIAGARA PENINSULA COLLEGE

Data File

Assessment 1   Creating a Table in Design View; Creating a Lookup Field

1. Open **2-NPCGrades.accdb** and enable the contents, if necessary.
2. Create a new table in Design view using the following field names: *StudentNo*; *LastName*; *FirstName*; *Grade*. Set the data type to *Short Text* for each field except *Grade*. At the *Grade* field, use the Lookup Wizard to create a drop-down list with the following grades: *A+, A, B, C, D, F*.
3. Restrict the *Grade* lookup properties to items within the list only and do not allow the values within the list to be edited from the datasheet.
4. Set the *StudentNo* field as the primary key field.
5. Save the table and name it AC478-01Grades.
6. Enter the following four records in the table in Datasheet view:

StudentNo	111-785-156		*StudentNo*	118-487-578
LastName	Bastow		*LastName*	Andre
FirstName	Maren		*FirstName*	Ian
Grade	A+		*Grade*	C
StudentNo	137-845-746		*StudentNo*	138-456-749
LastName	Knowlton		*LastName*	Yiu
FirstName	Sherri		*FirstName*	Terry
Grade	B		*Grade*	D

7. Adjust all column widths to best fit the longest entries.
8. Print and then close the AC478-01Grades table, saving changes.
9. Close **2-NPCGrades.accdb**.

 **Assessment 2** Changing Field Size; Validating Entries; Creating an
Input Mask; Formatting Dates; Formatting Data

Data File

1. Open **2-PTCostumeInv.accdb** and enable the contents, if necessary.
2. Open the CostumeInventory table in Design view.
3. Change the *DateIn* field to a Date/Time data type field.
4. Change the field size for *CostumeNo* to 5 characters to limit the field to the number of characters Performance Threads assigns to a costume inventory item.
5. Performance Threads has a minimum daily rental fee of $85.00. Create a validation rule and validation text entry that will ensure no one enters a value less than $85.00 in the *DailyRentalFee* field.
6. To ensure no one switches the order of the month and day when entering the *DateOut* and *DateIn* fields, create an input mask for these two fields to require that the date be entered in the Medium Date format.
7. Since Performance Threads is open seven days a week, format the *DateOut* and *DateIn* fields to display the dates in the Long Date format. This adds the day of the week to the entry and spells the month in full.
8. Save the table and then switch to Datasheet view.
9. Change the font size of the data in the table to 10 points and then adjust all column widths to best fit the longest entries. (Access displays pound symbols (#) across a column when the width is not wide enough to display the data.)
10. Preview the table. Change the margins for the page as necessary so that the entire table fits on one page.
11. Save, print, and then close the CostumeInventory table.
12. Close **2-PTCostumeInv.accdb**.

 **Assessment 3** Creating a New Database

1. Create a new database on your storage medium named **2-FCTExpenses**.
2. Look at the sample expense form in Figure WB-2.1. Make a list of the fields that would be needed to store the information from this form in a table. You do not need to include fields for the mailing address for the employee. For each field in your list, determine the appropriate data type and field properties that could be used.
3. Create a new table so that Access creates an *ID* field automatically that you can use as the primary key field. Use the design information you created in Step 2 to enter the field names, data types, and field properties in the table.
4. Switch to Datasheet view and then enter the expense claim information shown in Figure WB-2.1 in a record.
5. Make sure all column headings and data are entirely visible.
6. Display the table in Print Preview, make any necessary changes to ensure that the table will print on one page, and then print the table.
7. Close **2-FCTExpenses.accdb**.

Figure WB-2.1 Assessment 3

Expense Statement

Employee Information

Name:	Terry Blessing	Emp ID:	LA-104
Address:	3341 Ventura Boulevard	Position:	President
City, State, ZIP:	Los Angeles, CA 90102	Manager:	Not required

Expense Claim Details

Date	Description	TOTAL CLAIMED
3/26/2018	Travel expenses to Toronto office for meeting	$2,344.10

NOTE: All expense claims must have original receipts attached.

Signature_____

Assessment 4   Finding Information on Templates

1. Use the Help feature to find information on how to find and download a template and then read the article titled *Where do I find templates?* If this article is not available, determine how to search for templates at the New backstage area.
2. Search for a contact template. When contact templates display in the New backstage area, double-click one of the templates such as a personal contact manager template or a contacts template. (If a welcome window displays, click the Close button in the upper right corner of the window.) Enable the contents of the downloaded file.
3. If necessary, expand the Navigation pane by clicking the Shutter Bar Open/Close Button.
4. Open one of the tables in the database and then enter at least one record in the table. (You determine the data.)
5. Adjust all column widths to best fit the longest entries.
6. Print the table containing the record you entered.
7. Save the database with the name **2-Contacts**.
8. Close **2-Contacts.accdb**.

Assessment 5   Investigating Employment/Job Websites

1. Using the Internet, search for popular employment and/or job websites.
2. Create a new database on your storage medium named **2-JobWebsites**.
3. Create a table named *Websites* using Design view. Include fields to store the employment/job website name and the site's URL and then add a Long Text data type field in which you can type a brief note about the site's purpose. Include an *ID* field as the primary key field.

4. Save the table and then add at least three records to the datasheet for the sites you investigated in Step 1.
5. Preview and then print the Websites table, adjusting page layout options as necessary to minimize paper use.
6. Save and close the Websites table.
7. Close **2-JobWebsites**.

Marquee Challenge

Challenge 1 Modifying Tables and Creating a Table

1. Open **2-FCTTours.accdb** and enable the contents, if necessary.
2. Open the Tours table in Design view and then make the following changes:
   a. Move the *Tour* field between the *TourID* and *BegDate* fields.
   b. Delete the *Discount* field.
   c. Change the field size of the *TourID* field to 4 characters.
   d. This table contains tours only for the year 2019. Include a validation rule for the *BegDate* field that limits entries to dates after (greater than) 12/31/2018. Include appropriate validation text that will display if an incorrect date is entered in the field. Include a validation rule for the *EndDate* field that limits entries to dates before (less than) 1/1/2020. Include appropriate validation text that will display if an incorrect date is entered in the field.
   e. Enter the following records in the table. (Try entering incorrect dates in the *BegDate* and *EndDate* fields to determine if your validation rules work.)

TourID	HS04		*TourID*	BZ03
Tour	Hawaiian Special		*Tour*	Brazil Highlights
BegDate	4/3/2019		*BegDate*	4/24/2019
EndDate	4/9/2019		*EndDate*	5/4/2019
PriceSO	$1,899		*PriceSO*	$3,699
PriceDO	$1,659		*PriceDO*	$3,279

   f. Adjust column widths to best fit the longest enties.
   g. Save, print, and then close the Tours table.
3. Open the Agents table in Design view and then make the following changes:
   a. Delete the *HireDate* field.
   b. Change the field size of the *AgentID* field to 3 characters.
   c. Use the Lookup Wizard to specify the following choices for the *Office* field: *Los Angeles*, *San Francisco*, and *Toronto*.
   d. Enter the following records in the table:

AgentID	107		*AgentID*	131
FirstName	Jenna		*FirstName*	Rene
LastName	Williamson		*LastName*	Forbrege
OfficePhone	213-555-0939		*OfficePhone*	905-555-4321
CellPhone	562-555-3495		*CellPhone*	647-555-4389
Office	Los Angeles		*Office*	Toronto

4. Save, print, and then close the Agents table.

5. Create a new Bookings table with the fields shown below. You determine the field names and data types. Include appropriate captions for some or all of the fields. Change the field number size where appropriate and identify the *BookingID* field as the primary key field.

      BookingID (specify the AutoNumber data type and set as the primary key field)
      BookingDate (date the booking was made by the agent)
      TourID (the tour identification number from the Tours table)
      AgentID (the agent identification number from the Agents table)
      NumberPersons (number of people booked on a specific tour)

Include the following records in the table:

BookingID	(Access inserts number)	*BookingID*	(Access inserts number)
BookingDate	6/12/2018	*BookingDate*	6/14/2018
TourID	AF02	*TourID*	HC01
AgentID	114	*AgentID*	109
NumberPersons	8	*NumberPersons*	2

BookingID	(Access inserts number)	*BookingID*	(Access inserts number)
BookingDate	6/16/2018	*BookingDate*	6/16/2018
TourID	CR02	*TourID*	AK01
AgentID	103	*AgentID*	137
NumberPersons	2	*NumberPersons*	4

BookingID	(Access inserts number)	*BookingID*	(Access inserts number)
BookingDate	6/18/2018	*BookingDate*	6/19/2018
TourID	HC01	*TourID*	AT02
AgentID	109	*AgentID*	109
NumberPersons	2	*NumberPersons*	4

6. Save, print, and then close the Bookings table.
7. Create a one-to-many relationship that joins the Agents table with the Bookings table. (You determine the field that joins the two tables.) ***Hint: If you receive an error message when establishing a relationship, check to make sure that all the field types and field sizes are similar in the fields you are trying to join.***
8. Create a one-to-many relationship that joins the Tours table with the Bookings table. (You determine the field that joins the two tables.)
9. Create and print a relationship report and then close the Relationships window without saving the changes.
10. Close **2-FCTTours.accdb**.

Challenge 2   Refining Tables in a Database; Creating Relationships

Data File

1. Open **2-WEPurchases.accdb** and enable the contents, if necessary.
2. Open each table and look at the sample data entered and then, in Design view, modify field properties to maximize Access features that can control or otherwise validate data entered. Consider the following practices at Worldwide Enterprises as you complete this task:
   a. Worldwide uses a 4-character purchase order numbering system.
   b. All vendors are assigned a 3-character vendor number.
   c. Staff at Worldwide are used to entering dates in the format dd-mmm-yy.

d. Telephone numbers must include the area code in parentheses, for example, (212) 555-6549.

e. Worldwide will not issue a purchase order for corporate wear that has a value less than $300.00.

3. Set up a new field in the Purchases table to enter the shipment method. Worldwide will only receive shipments from the following carriers with whom credit accounts have been set up: UPS, FedEx, Express Freight, and Global Transport. After creating the new field, populate the existing records with one of the carrier companies to test the field.

4. Create a relationship between the Vendors table and the Purchases table.

5. Create and print a relationship report.

6. Print each table, making sure all data is visible and minimizing paper use.

7. Using Microsoft Word, create a memo to your instructor that documents the field properties you modified in each table, including the property box entry you made. Save the memo and name it **2-Memo**. Print and then close the memo. Close Word.

8. Close **2-WEPurchases.accdb**.

Creating Queries, Forms, and Reports

Study Tools

Study tools include a presentation and In Brief step lists. Use these resources to help you further develop and review skills learned in this section.

Knowledge Check

SNAP Check your understanding by identifying application tools used in this section. If you are a SNAP user, launch the Knowledge Check from your Assignments page.

Recheck

SNAP Check your understanding by taking this quiz. If you are a SNAP user, launch the Recheck from your Assignments page.

Skills Exercise

SNAP Additional activities are available to SNAP users. If you are a SNAP user, access these activities from your Assignments page.

Skills Review

Worldwide Enterprises

Review 1 Creating a Query Using the Simple Query Wizard; Sorting a Query; Performing Calculations; Extracting Records

Data File

1. Open **3-WEEmployeeData.accdb** and enable the contents, if necessary.
2. Use the Simple Query Wizard to create a query that displays fields from the Employees and Benefits tables in order as follows:

Employees	**Benefits**
EmployeeID	*LifeInsce*
FirstName	
LastName	
HireDate	
AnnualSalary	

3. Accept the default Detail query and then type LifeInsceList as the title for the query.
4. View the query results datasheet and then switch to Design view.
5. Sort the query results by the *LastName* field in ascending order.
6. Insert a calculation in the field to the right of *LifeInsce* that divides *AnnualSalary* by 12. Label the new column *MonthlySalary*.
7. Format *MonthlySalary* to display the calculated values in the Currency format.
8. Save and run the query and then adjust the column width of *MonthlySalary* to best fit the entries.

9. Print the query results datasheet with the left and right margins at 0.5 inch.
10. Use Save Object As to copy the query design and name it *HiresAfter2015*.
11. If necessary, switch to Design view and then type >December 31, 2015 in the field in the *Criteria* row in the *HireDate* column. ***Note: Access will convert the text you type to >#12/31/2015# after you press the Enter key***.
12. Save and then run the query.
13. Print the query results datasheet with the left and right margins set to 0.5 inch and then close the HiresAfter2015 query.

Review 2   Creating and Modifying a Form

1. With **3-WEEmployeeData.accdb** open, create a new form for the Review table using the Form button.
2. With the form open in Layout view, make the following changes to the form design:
   a. Add the logo named **WELogo-Small.jpg** to the top left of the form and then resize the image until the entire logo is visible.
   b. Change the title text to *Annual Review and Salary Increase Dates*.
   c. Change the font size of the title text to 20 points.
   d. Resize the text box control objects containing the data to align at the right edge of the objects below the right side of the word *Salary* in the title text. (The Status bar should display *Lines: 1 Characters: 24*.)
3. Save the revised form, accepting the default name *Review*.
4. Switch to Form view and then display the Print dialog box. Click *Selected Record(s)* in the *Print Range* section of the Print dialog box and then click OK.
5. Close the form. Click Yes if prompted to save changes to the form's design.

Review 3   Creating and Modifying a Report

1. With **3-WEEmployeeData.accdb** open, use the Report button to create a report based on the LifeInsceList query you created in Review 1.
2. With the report open in Layout view, make the following changes to the report design:
   a. Add the logo named **WELogo-Small.jpg** to the top of the report and then resize the image as needed until the entire logo is visible.
   b. Change the title text to *Salary and Life Insurance Report*.
   c. Change the font size of the title text to 20 points.
   d. Change to landscape orientation.
   e. Move the *Life Insurance* column between the *HireDate* and *AnnualSalary* columns. ***Hint: Select from the control object containing the column heading, Life Insurance, through the total row at the bottom of the column before moving the column***.
   f. Decrease the width of the *FirstName* and *LastName* columns approximately one inch. (The Status bar should display *Lines: 1 Characters: 12*.)
   g. Edit column heading labels for those field names that do not have a space between compound words. For example, change *FirstName* to *First Name*.
3. Apply the Integral report theme.
4. Click in the date control object and then press the Delete key. Click in the time control object and then press the Delete key.

5. Scroll to the bottom of the report. Select and then delete any totals that appear below columns and then select and delete the page number. *Note: You may also have to delete an underscore line before a total. To do this, click the field where the line appears and then press the Delete key.*

6. Display the report in Print Preview. Click the Columns button in the Page Layout group on the Print Preview tab. Select the current measurement in the *Width* measurement box, type 8, and then press the Enter key.

7. Save the report, accepting the default name *LifeInsceList*.

8. Print and then close the report.

9. Close **3-WEEmployeeData.accdb**.

Skills Assessment

Assessment 1 Creating a Query in Design View; Sorting a Query; Extracting Records Using Multiple Criteria

1. Open **3-NPCGrades.accdb** and enable the contents, if necessary.

2. Create a query in Design view that extracts the records of those students with an A+ grade in all three courses using the following specifications:

   a. Add all three tables to the query design grid and then drag the primary key field name from the first table field list box to the second table field list box. This creates a join line between the first two tables on the *StudentNo* field.

   b. Drag the primary key field from the second table field list box to the third table field list box to create a join line between the second and third tables on the *StudentNo* field.

   c. Include in the query results the student number, first name, last name, and grade from the first table field list box and sort in ascending order by last name.

   d. Add the grade field from the second and third tables to the query design grid.

   e. Enter the required criteria statements to select the records of those students who achieved A+ in all three courses. *Hint: Type A+ encased in quotation marks ("A+") in the* **Criteria** *row to indicate the plus symbol is not part of a mathematical expression*.

3. Save the query and name it *A+Students*.

4. Run the query.

5. Adjust the columns to best fit the entries in the query results datasheet.

6. Print the query results datasheet in landscape orientation.

7. Close the A+Students query, saving changes, and then close **3-NPCGrades.accdb**.

Assessment 2 Creating a Query and Report; Modifying a Report

1. Open **3-PTCostumeInv.accdb** and enable the contents, if necessary.

2. Create a new query in Design view using the CostumeInventory table that lists fields in the following order: *CostumeNo*, *DateOut*, *DateIn*, *CostumeTitle*, *DailyRentalFee*.

3. Type the following criterion statement in the *DateOut* column to extract records for costumes rented in the months of July and August 2018:

   Between July 1, 2018 and August 31, 2018

4. Expand the column width of the *DateOut* column to view the entire criterion statement. Access converted the long dates to short dates and added pound symbols to the beginning and end of dates in the criterion statement.

5. Sort the query results in ascending order first by the *DateOut* field.
6. Save the query and name it *Summer2018Rentals*.
7. Run the query.
8. Print and then close the query.
9. Create a report based on the Summer2018Rentals query using the Report button.
10. Add the logo image **PTLogo-Small.jpg** to the top of the report and then resize the image as needed so that the entire logo is visible.
11. Change the title text to *Costume Rentals for July and August 2018* and then change the font size to 20 points.
12. Delete the control objects containing the current date and current time.
13. Delete the total amount and underscore line at the bottom of the *DailyRentalFee* field column.
14. Adjust column widths in the report until all columns fit on the page in portrait orientation. Move and/or resize any other control objects as necessary so that the entire report fits on one page to print. ***Hint: Make sure you check the page numbering control objects at the bottom of the page***.
15. Save the report, accepting the default name *Summer2018Rentals*, and then print the report.
16. Close the report.

Assessment 3   Creating and Modifying a Form

1. With **3-PTCostumeInv.accdb** open, create a form for the CostumeInventory table.
2. Apply a theme of your choosing to the form.
3. Add the logo image **PTLogo-Small.jpg** to the top of the form and then resize the image as needed so that the entire logo is visible.
4. Change the title of the form. You determine appropriate title text and format.
5. Decrease the width of the control objects to improve the appearance and ensure the form will print on standard size paper.
6. Make any other changes you think are necessary to improve the form.
7. Save the form, accepting the default name *CostumeInventory*.
8. Display the first record in the table in Form view and then print the selected record, making sure the form fits on one page.
9. Close the form, saving changes, and then close **3-PTCostumeInv.accdb**.

Assessment 4   Finding Information on Creating a Form with a Subform

1. Use the Help feature to learn how Access creates a form when the table selected with the Form tool has a one-to-many relationship. ***Hint: Find and read the article titled* Create a form by using the Form tool**.
2. Open **3-WEVendors.accdb** and enable the contents, if necessary.
3. Open the Relationships window and observe that there is a one-to-many relationship between the Vendors (primary) and the Purchases (related) tables.
4. Close the Relationships window.
5. Create a new form using the Form button based on the Vendors table.
6. In Layout view, improve the appearance of the form by applying the skills you have learned in this section.
7. Display the first vendor record in Form view. Print the first record only, making sure the record will require only one page to print.
8. Close the form. Click Yes to save the form and accept the default form name.
9. Close **3-WEVendors.accdb**.

Assessment 5   Researching Movies on the Internet for a New Blog

1. You and your friends are thinking of starting a blog in which you will write reviews for current movies playing in your area. You decide you want to create a database to store records for all of the movies you and your friends will review. Choose four to six movies that are currently playing in your vicinity that you would like to review on your blog. Find the movie websites on the Internet. Look for the information listed in Step 3 that you will be entering into the new database.
2. Create a new database on your storage medium and name it **3-Movies.accdb**.
3. Create a table named *MovieFacts* that will store the following information (you determine the field names and field properties):

Movie Title	Lead Female Actor
Director's Name	Supporting Female Actor
Producer's Name	Movie Category: drama, action, thriller, and so on
Lead Male Actor	Movie Rating: G, PG, R, and so on
Supporting Male Actor	Website Address

4. Create a form to enter the records for the movies you researched. Modify the form by applying the skills you learned in this section.
5. Enter records for the movies you researched using the form created in Step 4.
6. Print only the first record displayed in Form view.
7. Create a report for the MovieFacts table. Modify the report by applying the skills you learned in this section.
8. Print the MovieFacts report.
9. Close **3-Movies.accdb**.

Marquee Challenge

The Waterfront BISTRO   Challenge 1   Creating Queries and a Report for a Catering Events Database

Data Files

1. Dana Hirsch, manager, has provided you with a copy of the database file used to track catering events at the bistro. Dana has been filtering records in the datasheet to obtain the lists needed for managing the events but is finding this process too time consuming. Dana has asked you to figure out how to create queries that can provide the information more efficiently. To begin, open **3-WBSpecialEvents.accdb** and enable the contents, if necessary.
2. Create the following queries:
   a. A WestviewEvents query that displays all events booked in the Westview room. In the query results datasheet, Dana would like the first and last names, the event type, the date the event is booked, the room booked for the event, the number of guests, and the special menu details. Print the query results datasheet using only one page with all column widths adjusted to best fit the entries.
   b. A JuneEvents query that displays all of the events booked in June 2018. In the query results datasheet, show the first and last names, the event type, the date the event is booked, and the room in which the event will be held. (You will need to set the criteria to display events booked between June 1, 2018 and June 30, 2018.) Print the query results datasheet with all column widths adjusted to best fit the entries.

c. An EventRevenue query that displays all records. In the query results datasheet, show the last name, the event type, the date the event is booked, the number of guests, and per-person charge. Calculate in the query the estimated revenue by multiplying the guests by the per person charge. You determine an appropriate column label and format for the calculated column. In the query results datasheet, add a total at the bottom of the calculated column. Print the query results datasheet using only one page and with all column widths adjusted to best fit the entries.

3. Create a report based on the EventRevenue query as shown in Figure WB-3.1 below. The company logo is stored in the file named **TWBLogo-Small.jpg**. Use your best judgment to determine the report formatting elements. The theme used is the default Office theme with individual formatting applied to headings. Apply the Dark Blue background color to the column headings and then apply bold formatting and White font color to the column heading text. Totals can be inserted at the bottom of columns by right-clicking the column heading for which a total is desired and then using options at the shortcut menu. Apply the same formatting to the total in the *Total Revenue* column that you applied to the column headings. Save the report using the default name.

4. Print the report, making sure you use only one page.

5. Close **3-WBSpecialEvents.accdb**.

Figure WB-3.1 Challenge 1

Last Name	Event	Date Of Event	Guests	Per Person Charge	Total Revenue
Hillmore	Business Meeting	1/15/2018	35	$21.95	$768.25
Fontaine	Engagement Party	1/20/2018	177	$28.95	$5,124.15
Corriveau	Birthday Party	1/23/2018	85	$25.95	$2,205.75
Kressman	Wedding	2/28/2018	266	$28.95	$7,700.70
Fagan	25th Wedding Anniversary	3/10/2018	88	$28.95	$2,547.60
Pockovic	Birthday Party	3/18/2018	62	$35.95	$2,228.90
Gill	Business Meeting	3/29/2018	71	$21.95	$1,558.45
Bresque	50th Wedding Anniversary	4/12/2018	62	$32.95	$2,042.90
Santore	Wedding	4/28/2018	157	$25.95	$4,074.15
Hamid	Engagement Party	5/8/2018	85	$28.95	$2,460.75
Torrance	Business Meeting	5/15/2018	26	$23.95	$622.70
Russell	Birthday Party	5/30/2018	36	$26.95	$970.20
Szucs	Birthday Party	6/10/2018	42	$28.95	$1,215.90
Griffin	25th Wedding Anniversary	6/17/2018	54	$31.95	$1,725.30
Doucet	Wedding	6/20/2018	168	$28.95	$4,863.60
Golinsky	Business Meeting	6/26/2018	57	$24.95	$1,422.15
Jin Ping	Baby Shower	7/10/2018	62	$21.95	$1,360.90
McMaster	Engagement Party	7/11/2018	75	$27.95	$2,096.25
Pavelich	Wedding	7/25/2018	110	$31.95	$3,514.50
Juanitez	Business Meeting	7/31/2018	49	$23.95	$1,173.55
			1767		$49,676.65

The Waterfront BISTRO — Catering Event Revenue — Monday, November 12, 2018 — 2:43:35 PM

 **Challenge 2** Creating a Form and Report for a Custom Costume Database

Data File

1. Bobbie Sinclair, business manager, is pleased with the way the custom costume database is taking shape. Bobbie would now like a form and a report created to facilitate data entry and printing of the custom orders. To begin, open **3-PTCostumes.accdb** and enable the contents, if necessary.
2. Create a form for the CostumeOrders table. You determine the layout and form design by applying skills you learned in this section.
3. With the first record displayed in Form view, print the selected record, making sure you use only one page. Save and close the form, saving changes and accepting the default form name.
4. Create a report to print the CostumeOrders table. You determine the layout and other elements of the report design by applying skills you learned in this section. Consider the example in Figure WB-3.2. In this report, the layout is changed to a stacked arrangement that allows all fields to print on one page since there are numerous fields in the table. To create your report with a similar layout to the one in Figure WB-3.2, explore options on the Report Layout Tools Arrange tab. The report in Figure WB-3.2 is a guide for layout purposes only. Your formatting may vary.
5. Save the report, accepting the default report name, and then print the report, making sure you minimize the amount of paper used.
6. Close **3-PTCostumes.accdb**.

Figure WB-3.2 Challenge 2

Study Tools

Study tools include a presentation and In Brief step lists. Use these resources to help you further develop and review skills learned in this section.

Knowledge Check

SNAP Check your understanding by identifying application tools used in this section. If you are a SNAP user, launch the Knowledge Check from your Assignments page.

Recheck

SNAP Check your understanding by taking this quiz. If you are a SNAP user, launch the Recheck from your Assignments page.

Skills Exercise

SNAP Additional activities are available to SNAP users. If you are a SNAP user, access these activities from your Assignments page.

Skills Review

Worldwide Enterprises

Data File

Review 1   Creating Crosstab, Find Unmatched, and Find Duplicates Queries

1. Open **4-WEEmployeeData.accdb** and enable the contents, if necessary.
2. Create a crosstab query that summarizes tuition payments by employee by quarter using the following information:
    a. At the first Crosstab Query Wizard dialog box, click the *Queries* option in the *View* section and then click *Query: TuitionReimbursed* in the list box.
    b. At the second Crosstab Query Wizard dialog box, specify that you want the *LastName* field as the row heading.
    c. At the third Crosstab Query Wizard dialog box, specify that you want the *Reimbursed* field as the column headings.
    d. At the fourth Crosstab Query Wizard dialog box, specify the quarter interval.
    e. At the fifth Crosstab Query Wizard dialog box, specify that you want to sum the tuition amounts.
    f. At the sixth Crosstab Query Wizard dialog box, name the crosstab query *TuitionByEmpByQtr*.
3. Add a total row to the query results datasheet and then sum each column.
4. Adjust column widths as necessary and then print the query results datasheet.
5. Save and then close the query.

6. Use the Find Unmatched Query Wizard to compare the Employees table with the Absences table and produce a list of employees who have not submitted absence reports. Display the fields *EmployeeID*, *FirstName*, and *LastName* in order in the query results. Name the query *NoAbsences*.
7. Print and then close the NoAbsences query results datasheet.
8. Create a find duplicates query that produces a list of employees who have submitted more than one absence report using the following information:
    a. At the first Find Duplicates Query Wizard dialog box, make sure *Table:Absences* is selected in the list box.
    b. At the second dialog box, move the *EmployeeID* field to the *Duplicate-value fields* list box.
    c. At the third dialog box, move all of the fields to the *Additional query fields* list box.
    d. At the final dialog box, name the query *DupAbsences*.
9. Print the DupAbsences query results and then close the query.

Review 2   Adding Control Objects to a Form; Sorting a Form
1. With **4-WEEmployeeData.accdb** open, open the Employees form in Layout view.
2. Insert the image file **Employees.jpg** below the entry in the *Department* field (below the text *North American Distribution*). Resize the image to approximately 2 inches in height.
3. Add a label control object in the column left of the image with the text *Contact the Help Desk at extension 436 if you need assistance using this form.*
4. Apply italic formatting to the text in the label control object added in Step 3.
5. Save the revised form and then switch to Form view.
6. Sort the records in Form view in descending order on the *HireDate* field.
7. With the first sorted record displayed, print the selected record only.
8. Save and then close the Employees form.

Review 3   Creating and Modifying a Report; Inserting a Calculation
1. With **4-WEEmployeeData.accdb** open, create a new report using the EmployeeList query.
2. Modify the report in Layout view as follows:
    a. Change to landscape orientation and then adjust column widths, leaving approximately 1 inch of space at the right side of the page for a new column.
    b. Insert a text box control object (label control object and text box control object) to the right of the *AnnualSalary* column. Using the *Control Source* property box in the Property Sheet task pane, type a formula that calculates the monthly salary by dividing *AnnualSalary* by 12. Apply currency formatting to the monthly salary amount. Type Monthly Salary in the label control object.
    c. If necessary, readjust column widths to ensure all data is visible and fits on one page.
    d. Delete the total and the line at the bottom of the *AnnualSalary* column.
    e. Edit the report title to read *Employee Salaries*.
    f. Delete the logo control object and the page numbering object at the bottom of the report.
    g. Click the table select handle to select all records in the report and then change the control padding to *None*.

    h. Move the date and time controls to align at the right edge of the last column.
    i. Add spaces between words in the column headings where necessary.
 3. Display the report in Print Preview. If necessary, switch to Layout view and make further adjustments to the size and/or position of the control objects.
 4. Save the report and name it *SalaryList*.
 5. Print and then close the report.
 6. Close **4-WEEmployeeData.accdb**.

Skills Assessment

Assessment 1   Inserting a Calculation in a Form

 1. Staff have commented positively on a form created for the inventory table; however, they would like the form modified to include the daily rental fee amount with the tax included. To begin, open **4-PTCostumes.accdb** and enable the contents, if necessary.
 2. Open the CostumeInventory form and review the current form layout and design.
 3. Insert a text box control object (label control object and text box control object) below the *DailyRentalFee* object. Using the *Control Source* property box in the Property Sheet task pane, type a formula that calculates the tax at 8% of the daily rental fee amount. Apply currency formatting to the tax amount. Type Tax Amount: in the label control object.
 4. Edit the labels for the other fields by inserting a space between words to improve the readability of the form.
 5. Display the form in Form view and then sort the records in descending order by the *Date Out* field. Print the first record only.
 6. Save and then close the CostumeInventory form.
 7. Close **4-PTCostumes.accdb**.

Assessment 2   Creating and Modifying a Report; Sorting a Report

 1. Open **4-WEDistributors.accdb** and enable the contents, if necessary.

 2. Create a new report using the CDN_Distributors table.
 3. Make the following modifications to the report.
    a. Change to landscape orientation.
    b. Edit the report title to read *Canadian Distributors by Province*.
    c. Delete the *StreetAdd2* and *EmailAdd* columns.
    d. Adjust the column widths so that the report uses only one page and all data is entirely visible.
    e. Edit the *StreetAdd1* column heading to *Street Address*. Add a space in the *CompanyName* column heading and the *PostalCode* column heading.
    f. Center-align all of the column headings.
    g. Delete the page numbering control object and any count or total control objects that Access automatically added to the bottom of the columns.
    h. Move the date and time controls to align at the right edge of the report.
    i. Using the logo control object, insert the image file named ***CanadaFlag.jpg***. Resize the image as necessary so that the entire flag is visible next to the title.
    j. Sort the report by the *Province* field in ascending order.
 4. Save the report, accepting the default name.

5. Print and then close the CDN_Distributors report. *Hint: Consider previewing the report before printing to make sure the report fits on one page. If necessary, delete any empty or unnecessary columns at the right edge of the report.*
6. Close **4-WEDistributors.accdb**.

Assessment 3 Creating Mailing Labels

1. Open **4-WEDistributors.accdb** and enable the contents, if necessary.
2. Create mailing labels using the CDN_Distributors table with the following specifications:
   a. Use Avery 5294 labels.
   b. Change the font to 10-point Garamond.
   c. Set up the prototype label for a proper mailing address.
   d. Sort the labels by the *PostalCode* field.
   e. Name the labels report *CDN_Labels*.
3. Print the labels and then close the report.
4. Close **4-WEDistributors.accdb**.

Assessment 4 Creating a Crosstab Query

1. Open **4-WBInventory.accdb** and enable the contents, if necessary.
2. Create a new query in Design view to calculate the aggregate Sum function with the following specifications:
   a. Insert the *SupplierCode* field from the InventoryList table field list box and the *Amount* field from the Purchases table field list box.
   b. Click the Totals button on the Query Tools Design tab and then sum the *Amount* field in the *Total* row.
   c. Save and then name the query *PurchasesBySupplierCode*.
   d. Run the query, adjust column widths as necessary, print the query results datasheet, and then close the query.
3. Create a crosstab query to sum the purchases by inventory item and by purchase date as follows:
   a. Base the crosstab query on the PurchaseItems query.
   b. Choose *ItemDescription* for the row headings.
   c. Choose *PurchaseDate* for the column headings and then use quarter intervals.
   d. Sum the *Amount* field.
   e. Accept the default query name.
   f. Add a *Total* row to the query results datasheet that sums each column. Adjust column widths as necessary.
   g. Print the query results datasheet and then save and close the query.
4. Close **4-WBInventory.accdb**.

Assessment 5 Finding Information on Creating a Query That Asks for Input

1. Use the Help feature to find out how to create a query that asks for input. *Hint: This type of query is called a* **parameter query**.
2. Open **4-WEEmployeeData.accdb** and enable the contents, if necessary.
3. Create a parameter query as follows:
   a. Add the Employees table to the query.

    b. Add the fields in this order: *EmployeeID*, *FirstName*, *LastName*, *HireDate*, and *Department*.

    c. Create a parameter that asks for the department name when the query is run.

    d. Save the query, naming it *PromptedDept*, and then close the query.

4. Open the PromptedDept query. When prompted for the department name, type Overseas Distribution and then press the Enter key.

5. Print the query results datasheet and then close the query.

6. Close **4-WEEmployeeData.accdb**.

INDIVIDUAL CHALLENGE **Assessment 6**   Researching Salary Statistics on the Internet and Creating a Blog Entry

1. You have decided to research current salaries for your field of study for a blog you will be writing on trends in your field at your school.

2. Search the Internet for current salary information by state or province for your field of study. Be sure to find consistent information for all states or provinces. For example, collect data that is based on the same unit, such as annual salary, hourly wage, or other unit of pay.

3. Create a new database and name it **4-SalaryStats**. Design and create a table to store the location and salary statistics that you found. Include a field to store the date you found the statistic references and another to describe the source agency or website from which you obtained the data.

4. Design and create a form for the table and then enter records for the locations you researched.

5. Design and create a report to print the records.

6. Save, print, and then close the report.

7. Close **4-SalaryStats.accdb**.

8. Write a short article in a Microsoft Word document that represents the content of a blog entry you would post on a social networking site that describes the salary data and the statistics you created. Save the Word document and name it **4-SalaryStatsBlog**. Print the document and then close Word.

Marquee Challenge

Data File

Challenge 1   Summarizing Catering Event Information

1. Dana Hirsch, manager of The Waterfront Bistro, has requested a summary report from the catering information database. Dana would like the summary report to group catering revenue by type of event and by date, in quarter intervals. In the report, Dana wants the data sorted in descending order by total revenue so that the highest-revenue events are listed first. Dana created a query that contains the fields and calculations needed but does not know how to group the data and has asked for your assistance. To begin, open **4-WBSpecialEvents.accdb** and enable the contents, if necessary.

2. Look at the report in Figure WB-4.1. The data is grouped by type of event in rows and by date of event in quarter intervals in columns.

3. Create a crosstab query to generate the data for the report. Name the query *RevByEventByQtr* and base it on the Revenue_and_Gratuity query.

4. Design and create a report similar to the one shown in Figure WB-4.1 based on the RevByEventByQtr query. Use your best judgment to determine the style and report formatting elements (delete the date, time, and page number content controls). The theme used is named *Ion* and the formatting incorporates theme colors. You will need to add totals at the bottom of columns, move a column, and center the title control object.
5. Name the report the same name as the source query.
6. Print the report.
7. Close **4-WBSpecialEvents.accdb**.

Figure WB-4.1 Challenge 1 Report

Revenue by Type of Event by Quarter

Event	Quarter 1	Quarter 2	Quarter 3	Total Revenue
25th Wedding Anniversary	$2,547.60	$1,725.30		$4,272.90
50th Wedding Anniversary		$2,042.90		$2,042.90
Baby Shower			$1,360.90	$1,360.90
Birthday Party	$4,434.65	$2,186.10		$6,620.75
Business Meeting	$2,326.70	$2,044.85	$1,173.55	$5,545.10
Engagement Party	$5,124.15	$2,460.75	$2,096.25	$9,681.15
Wedding	$7,700.70	$8,937.75	$3,514.50	$20,152.95
	$22,133.80	$19,397.65	$8,145.20	$49,676.65

 **Challenge 2** Summarizing Costume Rental Revenue with Conditional Formatting

Data File

1. Bobbie Sinclair, business manager for Performance Threads, has created a query in the costume inventory database that calculates the rental revenue from costumes in 2018. Bobbie would like a report from the query that groups the records by month. To begin, examine the partial report in Figure WB-4.2. This figure shows the first three months of activity in the rental revenue report for 2018. Open **4-PTCostumes.accdb** and enable the contents, if necessary.
2. Create a report named *RentalRevByMonth*, based on the RentalRevenue query.
3. Modify the report in Layout view to group as shown in the example in Figure WB-4.2. Conditional formatting is used in the *Days Rented* field to bold values that are greater than or equal to 40 days. Apply the Ion Boardroom theme and then use your best judgment to determine the formatting elements. *Hint: When a report is grouped on a date field, additional options are available in the Group, Sort, and Total pane to group by various time period intervals*.
4. Save, print, and then close the report. (The report is two pages.)
5. Close **4-PTCostumes.accdb**.

Figure WB-4.2 Challenge 2 Partial Rental Revenue Report

Costume Rental Revenue by Month

Date Out by Month	Costume No	Costume Title	Date In	Days Rented	Rental Fee
May 2018					
5/12/2018	S-101	Macbeth	6/30/2018	**49**	$9,115.47
5/2/2018	A-176	Pietro Gorski	6/10/2018	39	$4,774.77
5/12/2018	S-102	Lady Macbeth	6/30/2018	**49**	$10,128.30
5/2/2018	A-144	Kelly Williams	6/11/2018	**40**	$4,218.80
June 2018					
6/1/2018	A-152	Hannah Sorenti	7/12/2018	**41**	$5,019.63
July 2018					
7/7/2018	A-160	William Mercer	7/10/2018	3	$387.96
7/15/2018	A-110	Tony Salvatore	8/12/2018	28	$3,695.16
7/1/2018	D-105	Nala	7/31/2018	30	$6,002.25
7/7/2018	A-102	Eunice Billings	7/15/2018	8	$1,055.76
7/1/2018	D-107	Scar	7/31/2018	30	$6,320.25
7/22/2018	A-198	Nanci Lasertol	8/15/2018	24	$3,103.68
7/1/2018	D-101	Simba	7/31/2018	30	$7,147.05

Study Tools

Study tools include a presentation and In Brief step lists. Use these resources to help you further develop and review skills learned in this section.

Recheck

SNAP Check your understanding by taking this quiz. If you are a SNAP user, launch the Recheck from your Assignments page.

Skills Review

Review 1   Exporting Access Data to Excel

1. Open **2-PTCostumes.accdb** and then enable the contents.
2. Click *CostumeInventory* in the Tables group in the Navigation pane and then export the data to Excel in the Integrating2 folder on your storage medium with formatting and layout. Specify that you want the file to open after exporting.
3. Save the workbook as **2-CostumeInventory**.
4. When the data displays in Excel, make the following changes to the specified cells:
   C4: Change *110.00* to *120.00*.
   C5: Change *110.00* to *125.00*.
   C7: Change *99.50* to *105.00*.
5. Save, print, and then close **2-CostumeInventory.xlsx**.
6. Click the Access button on the taskbar.
7. Close the Export - Excel Spreadsheet dialog box and then close the database.

Review 2   Exporting Access Data to Word

1. Open **2-WBSupplies.accdb** and enable the contents.
2. Click *InventoryList* in the Tables group, export the table to Word in the Integrating2 folder specifying you want the file to open after exporting, and then save the file as **2-InventoryList**.
3. When the data displays in Word, make the following changes to the table:
   • Autofit the contents of the table.
   • Apply the List Table 3 - Accent 5 table style (sixth column, third row in the *List Tables* section).
   • Horizontally center the table on the page. ***Hint: Do this with the Properties button in the Table group on the Table Tools Layout tab.***
4. Move the insertion point to the beginning of the document (the insertion point will display in the first cell of the table), press the Enter key, and then type The Waterfront Bistro Inventory List.
5. Select *The Waterfront Bistro Inventory List*, change the font size to 20 points, apply bold formatting, and then center the text.

6. Save, print, and then close **2-InventoryList.rtf**.
7. Click the Access button on the taskbar.
8. Close the Export - RTF File dialog box and then close the database.

Review 3   Exporting an Access Report to Word

1. With Access active, open **2-PTCostumes.accdb** and, if necessary, enable the contents.
2. Click *CostumeInventory* in the Reports group in the Navigation pane, export it to a Word document in the Integrating2 folder, specifying you want the file to open after exporting, and then save the document as **2-CostumeInventory**.
3. If necessary, make Word active, change to landscape orientation, and apply Normal page margins.
4. Save, print, and then close **2-CostumeInventory.rtf**.
5. Close Word.
6. With Access active, close the Export - RTF File dialog box and then close the database.

Review 4   Importing Data to a New Table

1. In Access, open **2-PTCostumes.accdb** and, if necessary, enable the contents.
2. Import the Excel workbook named **PTCostumeHours.xlsx**. At the first Import Spreadsheet Wizard dialog box, make sure the *First Row Contains Column Headings* check box contains a check mark. Do not make any changes to the second dialog box. Click the *No primary key* option at the third dialog box. At the fourth dialog box, type DesignHours in the *Import to Table* text box and then click the Finish button. At the message asking if you want to save the import steps, click the Close button.
3. Open the new DesignHours table.
4. Print and then close the DesignHours table.
5. Close **2-PTCostumes.accdb**.

Review 5   Linking Data to a New Table and Editing Linked Data

1. Open Excel and then open the workbook **FCTBookings.xlsx**.
2. Save the workbook with the name **2-FCTBookings**.
3. Make Access active, open **2-FCTCommissions.accdb**, and then and enable the contents.
4. Link the Excel workbook **2-FCTBookings.xlsx** with the Access database **2-FCTCommissions.accdb**. (At the Get External Data - Excel Spreadsheet dialog box, click the *Link to the data source by creating a linked table* option. At the second Link Spreadsheet Wizard dialog box, type LinkedCommissions in the *Linked Table Name* text box.)
5. Open, print, and then close the new LinkedCommissions table.
6. Click the Excel button on the taskbar.
7. Make cell C2 active, type the formula =b2*0.03, and then press the Enter key.
8. Make cell C2 active and then use the fill handle to copy the formula down to cell C13.
9. Save, print, and then close **2-FCTBookings.xlsx**.
10. Click the Access button on the taskbar.
11. Open the LinkedCommissions table.
12. Save, print, and then close the LinkedCommissions table.
13. Close **2-FCTCommissions.accdb**.
14. Close Access and then close Excel.